This Orchard book belongs to

_____

_____

_____

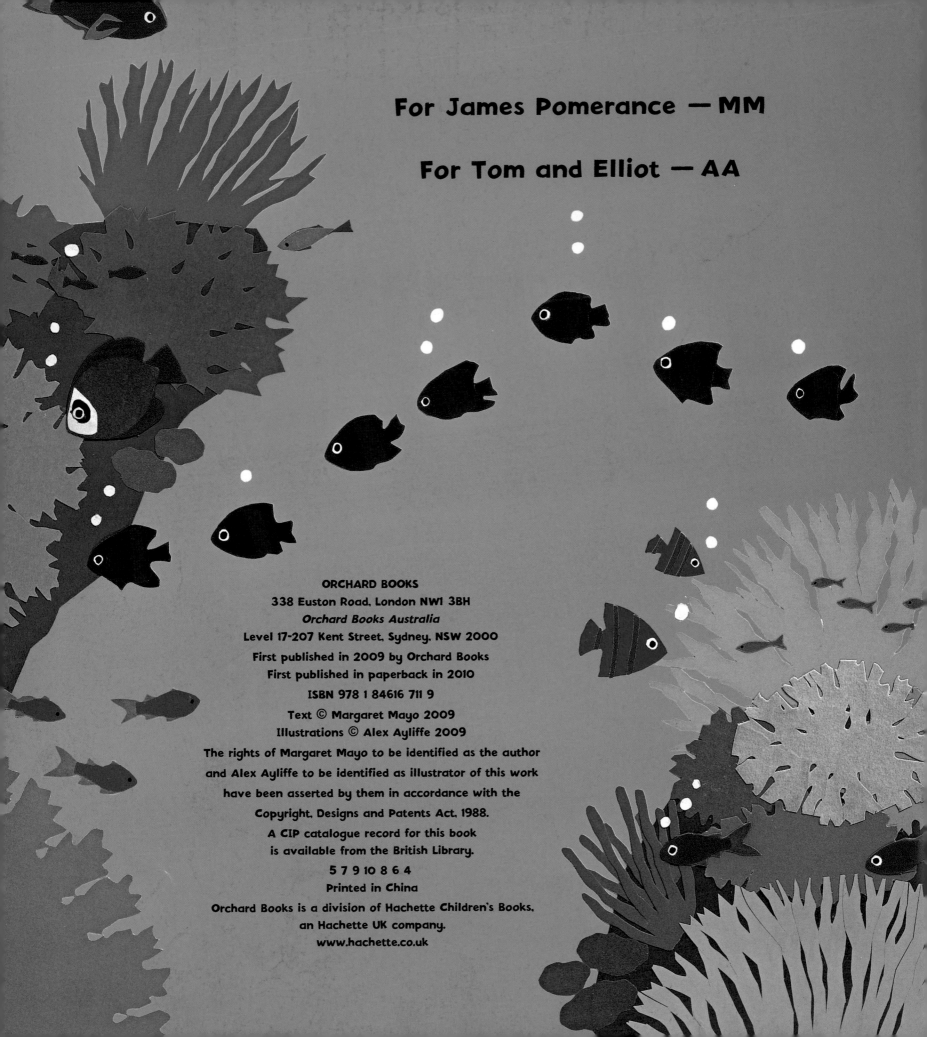

For James Pomerance — MM

For Tom and Elliot — AA

ORCHARD BOOKS
338 Euston Road, London NW1 3BH
Orchard Books Australia
Level 17-207 Kent Street, Sydney, NSW 2000
First published in 2009 by Orchard Books
First published in paperback in 2010
ISBN 978 1 84616 711 9
Text © Margaret Mayo 2009
Illustrations © Alex Ayliffe 2009

A CIP catalogue record for this book
is available from the British Library.
5 7 9 10 8 6 4
Printed in China
Orchard Books is a division of Hachette Children's Books,
an Hachette UK company.
www.hachette.co.uk

Margaret Mayo & Alex Ayliffe

SNAP!

ORCHARD

Sharks are good at snap, snap, snapping,
Whoosh! – dashing, tails lashing,
Spiky teeth ready for snap, snapping.
So snap, sharks, snap!

Dolphins are good at dance, dance, dancing,
High jumping, fast spinning,

Walrus are good at **waddle, waddle, waddling,**
As they huddle close, jostling, wibble–wobbling,

Making such a noise – blah! blah! – bellowing!
So waddle, walrus, waddle!

Whales are good at glide, glide, gliding,
Tails going up down, up down beating.

As they blast out air – pouffe! – tall spouts creating.

So glide, whales, glide!

Sea otters are good at float, float, floating.

Lying on their backs, shellfish scrunch, scrunching,

Little pups cradling and quietly snoozing.

So float, sea otters, float!

Penguins are good at dive, dive, diving, swooping, swerving, quick zig-zagging,

Tails and feet guiding, stiff wings **flip-flapping.**

So **dive,** penguins, **dive!**

Polar bears are good at **lollop, lollop, lolloping,**

With cubs following . . .

Slipping, sliding and **roly-polying!**
So **lollop**, polar bears, **lollop!**

Octopuses are good at waggle, waggle, waggling,

Arms waving, food grabbing, munch, munching,

And – squish! – jetting off, long arms trailing.

So waggle, octopuses, waggle!

Stingrays are good at underwater **flying,**
Wide fins **sweeping,** ripple, **rippling,**

Spindly tails flicking and . . . stinging!
So fly, stingrays, fly!

Seals are good at **play, play, playing,** chasing, dodging and . . . ooohh! . . . somersaulting,

Coming to the surface and **snorting**.

So **play**, seals, **play!**

Sea turtles are good at **dig, dig, digging,**
Sand scoop scooping, safe nests **making,**

Eggs laying . . . more digging! . . . covering and hiding.

So dig, sea turtles, dig!

All these creatures are good at swimming,
But they can never live on the shore.

A snapping shark is one such creature.
Now look carefully – can you find some more?